Contents

Step 1	**Two-digit × one-digit** no carrying	4
Step 2	**Two-digit × one-digit** carrying units to tens	6
Step 3	**Two-digit × one-digit** carrying units to tens	8
Step 4	**Three-digit × one-digit** carrying units to tens	10
Step 5	**Three-digit × one-digit** carrying tens to hundreds	12
Step 6	**Two-digit × one-digit** carrying tens to hundreds	14
Check-up test 1	**Two- and three-digit × one-digit, with up to one carried digit**	16
Step 7	**Two-digit × one-digit** carrying twice	18
Step 8	**Three-digit × one-digit** carrying twice with answers less than 1000	20
Step 9	**Three-digit × one-digit** carrying twice with answers greater than 1000	22
Step 10	**Three-digit × one-digit** carrying twice in any position	24
Step 11	**Four-digit × one-digit** with answers less than 10 000	26
Check-up test 2	**Two-, three- and four-digit × one-digit, carrying twice**	28
Step 12	**Four-digit × one-digit** carrying up to four times	30
Step 13	**Four- and five-digit × one-digit**	32
Step 14	**Six- and seven-digit × one-digit**	34
Check-up test 3	**Four-, five-, six- and seven-digit × one-digit**	36
Step 15	**Three-digit × 10 or × 20**	38
Step 16	**Three-digit × any two-digit multiple of 10**	40
Step 17	**Four- and five-digit × any two-digit multiple of 10**	42
Step 18	**Three- and four-digit × a multiple of 100 or 1000**	44
Final test	**Multiplying by one-digit numbers or by multiples of 10, 100 or 1000**	46

Step 1: Two-digit × one-digit no carrying

When learning to do written multiplication, it helps to work from right to left. Start with the units. To multiply 23 by 3, start by doing 3 × 3 first. Remember that zero multiplied by any number is zero.

	T	U
	2	3
×		3

What to do

23 × 3 = ?

1 Multiply the units digit of the top number by the bottom number. 3 × 3 = 9. Write the answer in the units column.

	T	U
	2	3
×		3
		9

2 Now, multiply the tens digit of the top number by the bottom number. 2 tens × 3 = 6 tens. Write the answer in the tens column.

	T	U
	2	3
×		3
	6	9

3 Check that the answer looks about right. *Three lots of 20 is 60, so three lots of 23 is a bit more than 60. The answer 69 seems about right.*

Now you try

1
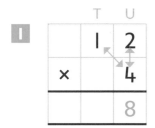

	T	U
	1	2
×		4
		8

2

	T	U
	3	1
×		3
		3

3

	T	U
	2	2
×		3

4

	T	U
	2	1
×		4

5

	T	U
	1	2
×		3

6

	T	U
	2	2
×		4

7

	T	U
	3	4
×		2

8

	T	U
	2	0
×		3

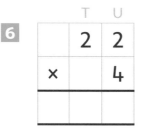

More practice

9
```
    2  3
×      2
_____
```

10
```
    3  3
×      3
_____
```

11
```
    2  4
×      2
_____
```

12
```
    3  0
×      3
_____
```

Set out these questions yourself to answer them.

13 11 × 5 = ?

T U
```
      |
×     |
_____
      |
```

14 44 × 2 = ?

T U
```
      |
×     |
_____
      |
```

15 32 × 3 = ?

T U
```
      |
×     |
_____
      |
```

16 11 × 6 = ?

T U
```
      |
×     |
_____
      |
```

Problem solving

17 Multiply 13 by 3.

_____

18 Jo buys two chocolate bars. Each costs 33p. How much does Jo pay?

_____

19 Find three lots of £21.

_____

20 Each bag contains 43 sweets. How many sweets are in two bags?

_____

How did I find Step 1?   ☐ Easy   ☐ OK   ☐ Difficult

Step 2: Two-digit × one-digit carrying units to tens

In these questions, when you multiply the units digit of the top number by the bottom number the answer is greater than 9.

Can you see that 9 × 3 here is 27?

	T	U
	2	9
×		3

What to do

$29 \times 3 = ?$

1 Multiply the units digit of the top number by the bottom number. 9 × 3 = 27. Think of each set of **10 units** as being **1 ten**. Rather than writing 27 in the units column write the 2 under the line in the tens column. This is called '**carrying**'. Write the 7 in the units column.

	T	U
	2	9
×		3
		7
	2	

2 Now, multiply the tens digit of the top number by the bottom number. 2 tens × 3 = 6 tens.

3 Before writing the answer, add on any tens you have carried. So here add 2 tens to the 6 tens to make 8 tens. Write 8 in the tens column.

	T	U
	2	9
×		3
	8	7
	2	

Now you try

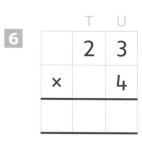

1

	T	U
	1	7
×		5
		5
	3	

2

	T	U
	2	4
×		4
		6
	1	

3

	T	U
	2	6
×		3
	1	

4

	T	U
	1	8
×		4

5

	T	U
	2	5
×		3

6

	T	U
	2	3
×		4

7

	T	U
	1	9
×		3

8

	T	U
	1	3
×		5

More practice

9

```
    1  6
×      4
————————
```

10

```
    1  8
×      5
————————
```

11

```
    2  7
×      3
————————
```

12

```
    1  9
×      4
————————
```

Set out these questions yourself to answer them.

13 17 × 4 = ?

T U

14 24 × 3 = ?

T U

15 19 × 5 = ?

T U

16 13 × 4 = ?

T U

Problem solving

17 What are five lots of 16?

_____

18 Three brothers each have £17.
How much do they have altogether?

_____

19 Multiply 16 by 3.

_____

20 In a school hall, the children put out five rows of chairs. There are 14 chairs in each row. How many chairs altogether?

_____

How did I find Step 2? ☐ Easy ☐ OK ☐ Difficult

Step 3: Two-digit × one-digit carrying units to tens

The questions on this page are answered in the same way as in Step 1 and Step 2, but include multiplying by 6, 7, 8 and 9. Not every question needs carrying. You must decide if it needs carrying or not.

What to do

$14 \times 6 = ?$

1 Multiply the units digit of the top number by the bottom number. $4 \times 6 = 24$. If the answer is more than 9, think of each set of 10 units as being 1 ten. Rather than writing 24 in the units column, carry the 2 under the line in the tens column. Just write the 4 units in the units column.

	T	U
	1	4
×		6
		4
	2	

2 Now, multiply the tens digit of the top number by the bottom number. 1 ten × 6 = 6 tens.

3 Before writing the answer, add on any tens you have carried. So here add 2 tens to the 6 tens to make 8 tens.

	1	4
×		6
	8	4
	2	

Now you try

Watch out as some questions do not need carrying at all!

1

		1	6
×			6
			6
		3	

2

		1	1
×			9
			9

3

		1	3
×			6
		1	

4

		1	2
×			7

5

		1	5
×			6

6

		1	2
×			8

7

		1	1
×			6

8

		2	3
×			4

More practice   Set out these questions yourself to answer them.

9 14 × 7 = ?   **10** 12 × 6 = ?   **11** 11 × 8 = ?   **12** 28 × 3 = ?

	T	U
×		

	T	U
×		

	T	U
×		

	T	U
×		

Problem solving

Each of these questions has a missing digit. Can you work out which digit is missing each time?

13
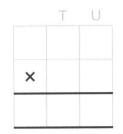

14

15
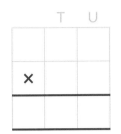

16
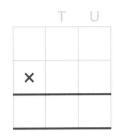

17 There are 32 children in a class.
Each child is given three pencils.
How many pencils are given out?

_____

18 Football teams have 11 players.
How many players are in seven teams?

_____

19 Apples cost 19p each. Malik buys five
apples and pays with a £1 coin.
How much change does he get?

_____

How did I find Step 3?   ☐ Easy   ☐ OK   ☐ Difficult

Step 4: Three-digit × one-digit carrying units to tens

For multiplying larger numbers, such as three-digit numbers, work in the same way as for earlier steps. Again, remember to work from right to left.

328×3

What to do

$328 \times 3 = ?$

1 Multiply the units digit of the top number by the bottom number. $8 \times 3 = 24$. If the answer is more than 9, think of each set of 10 units as 1 ten. Carry the 2 tens under the line and write 4 in the units column.

	H	T	U
	3	2	8
×			3
			4
		2	

2 Now, multiply the tens digit of the top number by the bottom number. 2 tens × 3 = 6 tens.

3 Before writing the answer, add on any tens you have carried. So here add 2 tens to the 6 tens to make 8 tens.

	H	T	U
	3	2	8
×			3
		8	4
		2	

4 Then multiply the hundreds digit by the bottom number. 3 hundreds × 3 = 9 hundreds.

	H	T	U
	3	2	8
×			3
	9	8	4
		2	

Now you try

1

	H	T	U
	2	1	5
×			4
			0
		2	

2

	H	T	U
	2	1	7
×			3
			1
		2	

3

	H	T	U
	1	1	9
×			5
		4	

4

	H	T	U
	3	2	6
×			3
			8

5

	H	T	U
	1	1	4
×			7

6

	H	T	U
	1	1	2
×			8

More practice

7

	2	2	5
×			3

8
	1	1	6
×			6

9
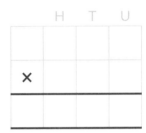

	1	0	6
×			8

Set out these questions yourself to answer them.

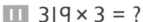

10 124 × 4 = ?

H	T	U
×		

11 319 × 3 = ?

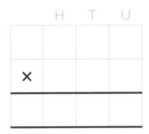

H	T	U
×		

12 107 × 6 = ?

H	T	U
×		

Problem solving

13 A school buys three new laptops. Each costs
£316. How much will they cost in total?

_____

14 Each day a factory makes 112 cars.
How many cars are made in seven days?

_____

15 A ball weighs 108g. How heavy are
six of these balls?

_____

How did I find Step 4?   ☐ Easy   ☐ OK   ☐ Difficult

Step 5: Three-digit × one-digit carrying tens to hundreds

So far, you have carried units over to the tens column. Sometimes, questions involve carrying tens over to the hundreds column.

What to do

$142 \times 3 = ?$

1 Multiply the units digit of the top number by the bottom number. $2 \times 3 = 6$. If the answer is less than 9, just write the answer in the units column.

	H	T	U
		1	4	2
×			3
			6

2 Now, multiply the tens digit of the top number by the bottom number. 4 tens × 3 = 12 tens. If the answer is more than 9, think of each set of **10 tens** as being **1 hundred**. Rather than writing 12 in the tens column, carry the 1 hundred under the line in the hundreds column. Just write the 2 tens in the tens column.

	H	T	U
		1	4	2
×			3
		2	6
	1		

3 Multiply the hundreds digit by the bottom number and remember to add any digits you have carried.
1 hundred × 3 = 3 hundreds. Add the carried hundred to get 4 hundreds and write 4 in the hundreds column.

	H	T	U
		1	4	2
×			3
	4	2	6
	1		

Now you try

1

H	T	U
	1	6	2
×			4
			8
2		

2

H	T	U
	2	9	3
×			3
			9
2		

3

H	T	U
	1	7	1
×			5
3		

4

H	T	U
	2	7	2
×			3
			6

5

H	T	U
	1	4	1
×			7

6

H	T	U
	1	5	1
×			6

More practice

7

	2	8	2
×			3

8

	2	4	1
×			4

9

	1	2	1
×			8

Set out these questions yourself to answer them.

10 121 × 7 = ?

H	T	U
×		

11 261 × 3 = ?

H	T	U
×		

12 181 × 5 = ?

H	T	U
×		

Problem solving

13 A person earns £271 per day for three days. How much money do they earn in total?

_____

14 Each day a factory makes 131 computers. How many computers are made in seven days?

_____

15 Find the product of 191 and 4.

_____

How did I find Step 5?	☐ Easy	☐ OK	☐ Difficult

Step 6: Two-digit × one-digit carrying tens to hundreds

With smaller numbers that have no hundreds to multiply, it is important to remember to write the carried number into the hundreds column. Don't forget it!

What to do

$42 \times 3 = ?$

	H	T	U
		4	2
×			3
			6

1   Multiply the units digit of the top number by the bottom number. $2 \times 3 = 6$. If the answer is less than 9, just write the answer in the units column.

	H	T	U
		4	2
×			3
		2	6
	1		

2   Now, multiply the tens digit of the top number by the bottom number. 4 tens × 3 = 12 tens. If the answer is more than 9, think of each set of 10 tens as being 1 hundred. Rather than writing 12 in the tens column, carry the 1 under the line in the hundreds column. Just write the 2 units in the tens column.

3   As the first number has no hundreds, you have no more multiplying to do, but you must write the carried digit in the hundreds column to finish your answer.

	H	T	U
		4	2
×			3
	1	2	6
	1		

Now you try

1	H	T	U
		6	3
×			3
			9
	1		

2	H	T	U
		3	1
×			9
			9
	2		

3	H	T	U
		7	1
×			6
			6
	4		

4	H	T	U
		5	1
×			7

5	H	T	U
		7	2
×			4

6	H	T	U
		8	1
×			5

7	H	T	U
		8	2
×			3

8	H	T	U
		9	1
×			8

More practice

Set out these questions yourself to answer them.

9 $43 \times 3 = ?$ **10** $31 \times 6 = ?$ **11** $61 \times 8 = ?$ **12** $82 \times 4 = ?$

 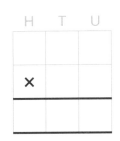 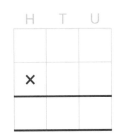 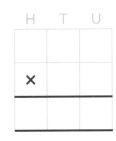

Problem solving

Each of these questions has a missing digit. Can you work out which digit is missing each time?

13

H	T	U
	◯	2
×		4
2	0	8
2		

14

H	T	U
	6	2
×		◯
1	8	6
1		

15

H	T	U
	◯	1
×		9
1	8	9
1		

16

H	T	U
	◯	1
×		7
4	9	7
4		

17 During fire practice the children in a school form three lines, with 73 children in each line. How many children are there altogether?

18 A shop sells coats costing £41 each. How much would the shop get if it sells seven of these coats?

How did I find Step 6?	☐ Easy	☐ OK	☐ Difficult

Check-up test 1 Two- and three-digit × one-digit, with up to one carried digit

Step 1

1 34 × 2 = ?

	3	4
×		2

2 32 × 3 = ?

	3	2
×		3

3 22 × 4 = ?

×		

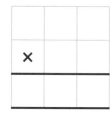

Steps 2 and 3

4 23 × 4 = ?

	2	3
×		4

5 17 × 5 = ?

	1	7
×		5

6 14 × 6 = ?

×		

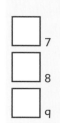

Step 4

7 114 × 7 = ?

	1	1	4
×			7

8 325 × 3 = ?

	3	2	5
×			3

9 124 × 4 = ?

×			

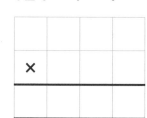

Step 5

10 131 × 7 = ?

	1	3	1
×			7

11 281 × 3 = ?

	2	8	1
×			3

12 162 × 4 = ?

×			

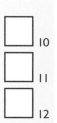

Step 6

13 52 × 4 = ?

	5	2
×		4

14 71 × 5 = ?

	7	1
×		5

15 31 × 6 = ?

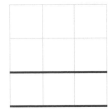

13
14
15

Steps 1 to 6 mixed

Use the grid below for working.

16 What is the cost of six 62p chocolate bars? _____ 16

17 How heavy are three 214g packets of biscuits in total? _____ 17

18 Multiply 141 by 7. _____ 18

19 What are four lots of 216kg? _____ 19

20 Find the product of 3 and 272. _____ 20

Total test score

Score	1	2	3	4	5	6	7	8	9	10	11	12	13	14	15	16	17	18	19	20
%	5	10	15	20	25	30	35	40	45	50	55	60	65	70	75	80	85	90	95	100

20

Step 7: Two-digit × one-digit carrying twice

Now that you have learnt to carry once, you can multiply and carry twice. Always work from right to left as before.

What to do

$57 \times 3 = ?$

1 Multiply the units digit of the top number by the bottom number. $7 \times 3 = 21$. Carry the 2 tens across and write the 1 in the units column.

	H	T	U
		5	7
×			3
			1
		2	

2 Now, multiply the tens digit of the top number by the bottom number. 5 tens × 3 = 15 tens. Add on the tens you have carried: 15 tens + 2 tens = 17 tens. Think of each set of 10 tens as being 1 hundred. Rather than writing 17 in the tens column, carry the 1 under the line in the hundreds column. Just write the 7 tens in the tens column.

		5	7
×			3
		7	1
	1	2	

3 As the first number has no hundreds, you have no more multiplying to do, but you must write the carried digit in the hundreds column to finish your answer.

		5	7
×			3
	1	7	1
	1	2	

Now you try

1

	3	7
×		5
		5
1	3	

2

	4	4
×		9
		6
	3	

3

	7	5
×		6
		0
	3	

4

	9	4
×		7
		8

5

	3	8
×		4

6

	8	4
×		5

7

	8	6
×		3

8

	9	4
×		8

More practice

Set out these questions yourself to answer them.

9 $46 \times 3 = ?$

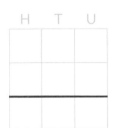

10 $54 \times 6 = ?$

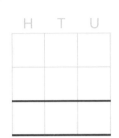

11 $62 \times 8 = ?$

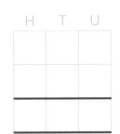

12 $78 \times 4 = ?$

Problem solving

Each of these questions has a missing digit. Can you work out which digit is missing each time?

13

	○	4
×		4
2	1	6
2	1	

14

	6	7
×		○
2	0	1
2	2	

15

	4	○
×		9
4	0	5
4	4	

16

	○	4
×		7
5	1	8
5	2	

17 Six children each raised £48 for charity.
How much did they raise altogether?

18 A factory makes 63 bikes per hour.
How many does it make in eight hours?

Step 8: Three-digit × one-digit carrying twice with answers less than 1000

These questions involve carrying twice in the same way as for Step 7. The answers here are always three-digit numbers.

What to do

$258 \times 3 = ?$

1 Do the same as in Step 7. Multiply the units digit first and remember to carry any tens over. $8 \times 3 = 24$

	H	T	U
		2	5	8
×				3
				4
			2	

2 Then multiply the tens digit and remember to add the carried tens to the answer. 5 tens × 3 = 15 tens, 15 tens plus the 2 tens carried = 17 tens. Think of each set of 10 tens as 1 hundred and carry it across to the hundreds column.

	2	5	8
×			3
		7	4
1	2		

3 Now, multiply the hundreds digit. 2 hundreds × 3 = 6 hundreds. Add on any hundreds that you have carried. 6 hundreds + 1 hundred = 7 hundreds. Write this in the hundreds column.

	2	5	8
×			3
	7	7	4
1	2		

Now you try

1

	2	4	7
×			3
			1
	1	2	

2

	1	5	2
×			6
			2
	3	1	

3

	1	3	7
×			5
			5
		3	

4

	2	4	7
×			4
			8
	2		

5

	1	3	7
×			6
			2

6

	1	1	9
×			8
			2

More practice

7
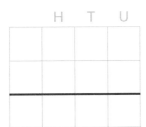

	2	8	5
×			3

8
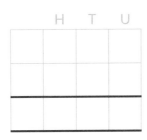

	1	3	5
×			6

9
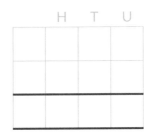

	1	2	9
×			7

Set out these questions yourself to answer them.

10 234 × 4 = ?

H T U

11 279 × 3 = ?

H T U

12 136 × 6 = ?

H T U

Problem solving

13 A helicopter travels 245km each hour for three hours. How far does it travel?

14 Each day a machine makes 142 laptops. How many are made in seven days?

15 Find the product of 134 and 7.

How did I find Step 8? ☐ Easy ☐ OK ☐ Difficult

Step 9: Three-digit × one-digit carrying twice with answers greater than 1000

Sometimes, you need to carry to the thousands column.

What to do

$917 \times 5 = ?$

1 Multiply the units digit and carry any tens over. $7 \times 5 = 35$

	Th	H	T	U
		9	1	7
×				5
				5
			3	

2 Then multiply the tens digit and add the carried tens to the answer. 1 ten × 5 = 5 tens, 5 tens plus the 3 tens carried = 8 tens. Here, you don't need to carry at all as the answer is not greater than 9 tens.

	H	T	U
	9	1	7
×			5
		8	5
		3	

3 Now, multiply the hundreds digit. 9 hundreds × 5 = 45 hundreds. Think of each set of **10 hundreds** as **1 thousand**. Rather than writing 45 in the hundreds column carry the 4 thousands under the line in the thousands column and write the 5 hundreds in the hundreds column.

	H	T	U
	9	1	7
×			5
	5	8	5
4		3	

4 As the first number has no thousands, you have no more multiplying to do, but you must write the carried digit in the thousands column to finish your answer.

	H	T	U
	9	1	7
×			5
4	5	8	5
4		3	

Now you try

1

Th	H	T	U
	7	1	8
×			4
		7	2
2		3	

2

Th	H	T	U
	5	2	9
×			3
			7
		2	

3

Th	H	T	U
	6	1	9
×			5
			5
		4	

 4

	4	1	2
×			6
		1	

5

	3	1	3
×			7

6

	6	0	5
×			8

More practice

7

	9	1	8
×			3

8

	4	1	5
×			4

9

	7	0	9
×			9

Problem solving

A palindromic number is one that is the same when read forwards or backwards, for example 626.

10 Write as many three-digit palindromic numbers as you can that have the tens digit 1, such as 717, 818, 313.

	1	

_____

11 Multiply each of the palindromic numbers by 4 and write the answers in ascending order. Use spare squared paper for workings.

_____

Answer 'yes' or 'no' to each question.

12 Is the hundreds digit and unit digit the same in each answer? _____

13 Is 2646 one of the answers? _____

14 Are there three answers that have the thousands digit 2? _____

15 Are there three answers that have the tens digit 5? _____

| How did I find Step 9? | Easy | OK | ☐ Difficult |

Step 10: Three-digit × one-digit carrying twice in any position

For this step, you will need to work out when to carry and when not to. The carrying will not always be in the same place.

What to do

$941 \times 5 = ?$

1 Multiply the units digit and carry any tens over.

Th	H	T	U
	9	4	1
×			5
			5

2 Then multiply the tens digit, adding any carried tens if there are any. Carry over to the hundreds if you need to.

	9	4	1
×			5
		0	5
		2	

3 Then multiply the hundreds digit, adding any carried hundreds if there are any.

	9	4	1
×			5
	7	0	5
4	2		

4 As the first number has no thousands, you have no more multiplying to do, but you must write any carried thousands digits (if there are any) in the thousands column to finish your answer.

	9	4	1
×			5
4	7	0	5
4	2		

Now you try

1

	7	6	2
×			4
		4	8
	3	2	

2

	1	2	9
×			6
			4
		5	

3

	8	4	3
×			3
		2	9
		1	

4

	7	1	2
×			5
		1	

5

	3	4	1
×			7
			7

6

	7	0	6
×			8

More practice

7

	8	6	2
×			3

8

	2	2	7
×			4

9

	4	0	6
×			9

Problem solving

Each of these questions has two missing digits. Can you work out which digits are missing each time?

10

	8	○	3
×			2
1	○	2	6
	1	1	

11

	○	6	1
×			4
3	0	○	4
	3	2	

12 A plane travels 824km each hour for three hours. How far does it travel?

13 Multiply 138 by 7.

14 How many eggs are there in 316 boxes of six eggs?

15 Each DVD in a shop is sold for £7. How much does the shop get if it sells 251 DVDs?

How did I find Step 10? ☐ Easy ☐ OK ☐ Difficult

Step 11: Four-digit × one-digit with answers less than 10 000

For these questions, you must remember to multiply the thousands digit as you will be multiplying four-digit numbers.

What to do

$1527 \times 3 = ?$

1   As before, multiply the units digit and carry any tens over.

Th	H	T	U
	1	5	2	7
×				3
				1
			2	

2   Then multiply the tens digit, adding any carried tens if there are any. Carry over to the hundreds if you need to.

Th	H	T	U
	1	5	2	7
×				3
			8	1
			2	

3   Then multiply the hundreds digit, adding any carried hundreds if there are any.

Th	H	T	U
	1	5	2	7
×				3
		5	8	1
	1		2	

4   Then multiply the thousands digit, adding any carried digits (if there are any) in the thousands column to finish your answer. The thousands digit of your answer will **not** be the same as the carried digit (as it was in Step 10).

Th	H	T	U
	1	5	2	7
×				3
4	5	8	1
1		2	

Now you try

1

Th	H	T	U
	1	6	3	7
×				2
			7	4
			1	

2

Th	H	T	U
	2	5	8	1
×				3
				3
		2		

3

Th	H	T	U
	1	4	1	3
×				7
				1
		2		

4

Th	H	T	U
	2	4	1	5
×				4
				0

5

Th	H	T	U
	1	4	7	1
×				5

6

Th	H	T	U
	1	5	0	8
×				6

More practice

Set out these questions yourself to answer them.

7 2863 × 3 = ?

8 1614 × 4 = ?

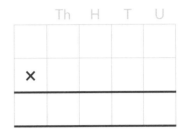

9 1421 × 6 = ?

Th H T U

10 1904 × 5 = ?

Th H T U

Problem solving

11 A relay team consists of six cyclists. Each cyclist cycles 1341m. How far does the team cycle in total?

12 A cinema holds 1408 people. For seven nights it was full. How many people went to the cinema that week?

| How did I find Step 11? | ☐ Easy | ☐ OK | ☐ Difficult |

Check-up test 2 Two-, three- and four-digit × one digit, carrying twice

Step 7

1 56 × 3 = ?

		5	6
×			3

2 94 × 7 = ?

		9	4
×			7

3 74 × 4 = ?

×			

1

2

3

Step 8

4 249 × 3 = ?

	2	4	9
×			3

5 164 × 4 = ?

	1	6	4
×			4

6 127 × 7 = ?

4

5

6

Step 9

7 917 × 5 = ?

	9	1	7
×			5

8 824 × 4 = ?

×			

7

8

Step 10

9

	8	5	3
×			3

10

	7	1	2
×			8

9

10

Step 11

11 1481 × 4 = ?

	1	4	8	1
×				4

12 1815 × 5 = ?

☐ 11
☐ 12

Steps 7 to 11 mixed

Use the grid below for working.

13 What is the cost of four £63 games?   _____   ☐ 13

14 What is the total length of a piece of ribbon cut into three 285cm lengths?   _____   ☐ 14

15 Multiply 416 by 4.   _____   ☐ 15

16 How many eggs are in 314 boxes of six eggs?   _____   ☐ 16

17 Find the product of 3 and 2732.   _____   ☐ 17

Total test score

Score	1	2	3	4	5	6	7	8	9	10	11	12	13	14	15	16	17
%	6	12	18	24	29	35	41	47	53	59	65	71	76	82	88	94	100

17

Step 12: Four-digit × one-digit carrying up to four times

Carrying should be done whenever you multiply a digit and get an answer that is greater than 9. Here, you'll carry when multiplying every digit.

What to do

$5847 \times 3 = ?$

1 As before, multiply the units digit and carry any tens over. $7 \times 3 = 21$. Carry the 2 tens.

	TTh	Th	H	T	U
		5	8	4	7
×					3
					1
				2	

2 Then multiply the tens digit, adding the carried tens. 4 tens × 3 = 12 tens, 12 tens + 2 tens = 14 tens. Carry the 1 hundred.

	Th	H	T	U
	5	8	4	7
×				3
			4	1
		1	2	

3 Then multiply the hundreds digit, adding the carried hundreds. 8 hundreds × 3 = 24 hundreds. 24 hundreds + 1 hundred = 25 hundreds. Carry the 2 thousands.

	Th	H	T	U
	5	8	4	7
×				3
		5	4	1
	2	1	2	

4 Then multiply the thousands digit, adding the carried thousands. 5 thousands × 3 = 15 thousands, 15 thousands + 2 thousands = 17 thousands. Carry the 1 ten thousand.

	Th	H	T	U
	5	8	4	7
×				3
	7	5	4	1
1	2	1	2	

5 As the first number has no ten thousands, you have no more multiplying to do, but you must write any carried ten thousands digits above to finish your answer.

	TTh	Th	H	T	U
		5	8	4	7
×					3
	1	7	5	4	1
		2	1	2	

Now you try

1

		3	2	4	7
×					5
				3	5
			2	3	

2

		6	3	8	4
×					4
				3	6
				1	

3

		6	2	3	8
×					6
					8
				4	

4

		9	3	2	7
×					9
				6	

More practice

Set out these questions yourself to answer them.

5 5243 × 8 = ?

6 1925 × 7 = ?

7 7777 × 5 = ?

8 1234 × 9 = ?

Problem solving

9 Choose an even number and repeat it four times to make a four-digit number, for example 6666. Multiply the number by 5. Do this several times. Write what you notice about the digits of the answer.

10 A theatre holds 5735 people. For seven nights it was full. How many people went to the theatre that week?

| How did I find Step 12? | Easy | ☐ OK | ☐ Difficult |

Step 13: Four- and five-digit × one-digit

When calculating, it is good practice to make an estimate first and then use it to check your answer. For these questions, you'll have to decide whether you need to carry digits or not. Some also involve five-digit numbers.

What to do

30645 × 5 = ?

1 For each of these questions, make an estimate first.

2 As before, work from right to left, carrying if you need to.

3 Check your final answer against your estimate and see if your answer seems reasonable. Is 153 225 close to 150 000?

30 000 × 5 = 150 000

	TTh	Th	H	T	U
	3	0	6	4	5
×					5
1	5	3	2	2	5
	1		3	2	2

Now you try

Remember to make an estimate first.

1 20 000 × 3 = _____

	TTh	Th	H	T	U
	2	1	7	9	5
×					3
				8	5
				2	1

2 40 000 × 5 = _____

	TTh	Th	H	T	U
	3	9	8	1	6
×					5
				8	0
				3	

3 10 000 × 7 = _____

	TTh	Th	H	T	U
		9	8	1	4
×					7
					8
				2	

4 _____ × 8 = _____

	TTh	Th	H	T	U
	3	0	1	6	1
×					8

More practice

Make an estimate for each question and use it to check whether an error has been made.
Circle each of the errors in the answers and correct them.

5 _____

		3	9	8	6
×					8
	1	1	8	8	8
		3	7	6	4

6 _____

		5	1	3	2
×					9
		6	1	8	8
			1	2	1

7 _____

	2	9	7	8	6
×					6
1	2	8	7	1	6
1	5	4	5	3	

8 _____

		5	0	2	7
×					7
	3	5	8	8	9
		3		1	4

Problem solving

9 Jack earns £26454 each year for
two years. How much does he earn?

10 Find the total of 4172 × 6 and 3626 × 8.

Step 14: Six- and seven-digit × one-digit

What to do

1 You've mastered multiplying by single-digit numbers, so now try it for even larger numbers!

2 Follow the same approach as before and remember to estimate first.

M	HTh	TTh	Th	H	T	U
	2	5	3	0	6	4	8
×							5
1 2	6	5	3	2	4	0
1 2 1			3	2	4	

Now you try

Remember to make an estimate first and use it to check your final answer.

1 Five hundred and thirty thousand, six hundred and forty-five times four.

$500\,000 \times 4 =$ _____

	M	HTh	TTh	Th	H	T	U
		5	3	0	6	4	5
×							4
						8	0
					1	2	

2 Two million, one hundred and nineteen thousand and twelve times three.

$2\,000\,000 \times 3 =$ _____

	M	HTh	TTh	Th	H	T	U
		2	1	1	9	0	1	2
×							3
						3	6

3 Nine hundred and seventeen thousand, eight hundred and seven times six.

$900\,000 \times 6 =$ _____

	M	HTh	TTh	Th	H	T	U
		9	1	7	8	0	7
×							6
						4	2
						4	

4 Seven million and forty-one thousand, seven hundred and eighty-one times nine.

$7\,000\,000 \times 9 =$ _____

	M	HTh	TTh	Th	H	T	U
		7	0	4	1	7	8	1
×							9
						2	9

More practice   Use the grids below for working. Remember to estimate first.

5 Two hundred and ten thousand, nine hundred and seven times three.

_____

6 Three million, eight hundred and fourteen thousand and six times two.

_____

7 Four hundred and sixty-one thousand, six hundred and twelve times eight.

_____

8 Six million, eight hundred and three thousand and thirty times seven.

_____

Problem solving

9 Multiply several numbers made from six or seven consecutive digits by 9, for example 1234567 × 9 or 3456789 × 9. Write any patterns you notice.

_____

_____

How did I find Step 14?   ☐ Easy   ☐ OK   ☐ Difficult

Check-up test 3 Four-, five-, six- and seven-digit × one digit

Step 12

1 9327 × 5 = ?

	9	3	2	7
×				5

2 4322 × 9 = ?

☐ ₁
☐ ₂

Step 13

3 31 461 × 6 = ?

	3	1	4	6	1
×					6

4 29 156 × 4 = ?

☐ ₃
☐ ₄

Step 14

5 Two million, one hundred and twelve thousand, three hundred and six times five.

	2	1	1	2	3	0	6
×							5

☐ ₅

6 Five million, two hundred and thirty thousand, six hundred and forty-five times nine.

☐ ₆

Steps 12 to 14 mixed

Use the grids below for working.

7 Seven people each win £6473 on the lottery.
What is their total win?   _____   ☐ 7

8 Taking a year to be 525 600 minutes, how many
minutes are there in seven years?   _____   ☐ 8

9 Which is greater: 123 456 × 6 or 234 567 × 3?

_____   ☐ 9

10 If an aeroplane travels 15 750 km per week,
how far will it travel in six weeks?   _____   ☐ 10

Total test score   ☐ 10

Score	1	2	3	4	5	6	7	8	9	10
%	10	20	30	40	50	60	70	80	90	100

Step 15: Three-digit × 10 or × 20

When multiplying by 10, the digits of the number being multiplied move one place to the left. Here, we need to put a zero in the units column to complete the answer. Now read how to multiply by 20.

Th	H	T	U
	2	3	7
×		1	0
2	3	7	**0**

What to do

$237 \times 20 = ?$

1 To multiply by 20, first write zero in the units column.

Th	H	T	U
	2	3	7
×		2	0
			0

2 Then multiply the top number by 2, in the same way as before, but writing the digits of the answer one place to the left. Start by multiplying the units digit by 2, so 7 × 2 = 14. Carry 1 across and write the 4.

Th	H	T	U
	2	3	7
×		2	0
		4	**0**

3 Now, multiply the tens digit and add the carried ten.

4 Then multiply the hundreds digit and add any carried digits.

Th	H	T	U
	2	3	7
×		2	0
4	7	4	**0**

5 Check your answer is the same as doubling the number and then multiplying by 10.

Now you try

1

		3	1	8
×			1	0
			8	**0**

2

		8	4	7
×			1	0
				0

3

		3	1	8
×			2	0
			6	**0**

4

		4	7	9
×			2	0
			8	**0**

5

		8	3	6
×			2	0
				0

6

		7	8	7
×			2	0
				0

More practice

7

		6	8	7
×			2	0

8

		8	9	3
×			2	0

Set out these questions yourself to answer them.

9 $472 \times 20 = ?$

TTh	Th	H	T	U

10 $586 \times 20 = ?$

TTh	Th	H	T	U

Problem solving

Work out which of these answers are correct and which are wrong.
Find the correct answers for those that are wrong.

11 $127 \times 20 = 254$

_____

12 $432 \times 20 = 8640$

_____

13 $567 \times 20 = 11\,340$

_____

14 $845 \times 20 = 1690$

_____

How did I find Step 15?	☐ Easy	☐ OK	☐ Difficult

Step 16: Three-digit × any two-digit multiple of 10

Now that you can multiply by 10 or 20, you can multiply by 30, 40, 50 or any other two-digit multiple of 10.

$638 × 40$

What to do

$638 × 40 = ?$

1 As you are multiplying by a multiple of 10, first write zero in the units column.

TTh	Th	H	T	U
		6	3	8
×			4	0
				0

2 Then multiply the three-digit number by the other digit of the multiple of 10, here by 4, writing the digits of the answer one place to the left. Start with the units as before. 8 × 4 = 32. Carry 3 across and write the 2.

		6	3	8
×			4	0
			2	**0**
			3	

3 Now, multiply the tens digit and add the carried digit. Carry 1 across and write the 5.

		6	3	8
×			4	0
		5	2	**0**
		1	3	

4 Then multiply the hundreds digit, add the carried digit and complete your answer.

		6	3	8
×			4	0
2	5	5	2	**0**
2	1	3		

Now you try

1

		8	3	6
×			4	0
			4	**0**
		2		

2

		7	8	7
×			9	0
			3	**0**
		6		

3

		9	3	5
×			3	0
			5	**0**

4

		7	8	7
×			8	0
				0

More practice

5
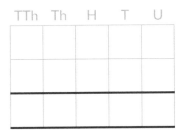

		7	4	5
×			6	0

6
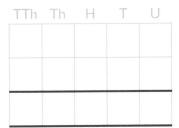

		4	9	1
×			7	0

Set out these questions yourself to answer them.

7 888 × 50 = ?

TTh	Th	H	T	U

8 664 × 90 = ?

TTh	Th	H	T	U

Problem solving

9 Multiply 678 by 30.

_____

10 Taking a year to be 365 days, how many days are there in 50 years?

_____

11 Find 70 lots of 587.

_____

12 Each person on a plane has paid £60 for their ticket. If there are 264 people on the plane, how much was paid?

_____

 **How did I find Step 16?**   Easy   OK   Difficult

Step 17: Four- and five-digit × any two-digit multiple of 10

Multiplying four- or five-digit numbers by a multiple of 10 is just the same!

What to do

$10642 \times 70 = ?$

1 As you are multiplying by a multiple of 10, first write zero in the units column.

HTh	TTh	Th	H	T	U
	1	0	6	4	2
×				7	0
					0

2 Then multiply the large number by the other digit of the multiple of 10, here by 7, writing the digits of the answer one place to the left. Start with the units. 7 × 2 = 14. Carry 1 across and write the 4.

	1	0	6	4	2
×				7	0
				4	**0**
			1		

3 Now, multiply the tens digit and add the carried digit. Carry 2 across and write the 9.

	1	0	6	4	2
×				7	0
			9	4	**0**
		2	1		

4 Then multiply the hundreds digit, add the carried digit and continue in this way to complete your answer.

	1	0	6	4	2
×				7	0
7	4	4	9	4	**0**
	4	2	1		

Now you try

1

	1	0	7	9	5
×				9	0
				5	**0**
			4		

2

		5	8	8	6
×				4	0
				4	**0**
			2		

3

	3	0	6	4	5
×				6	0
				0	**0**
			3		

4

	3	2	9	7	5
×				8	0
				0	**0**

More practice

Use the grids below for working.

5 8624 × 30 = ? _____

6 14644 × 70 = ? _____

7 61 632 × 50 = ? _____

8 57886 × 90 = ? _____

Problem solving

9 A group of 30 people won the lottery. They each got £4634. What was the total lottery win?

_____

10 There are 8760 hours in a normal year. Taking each year to be the same, how many hours are there in 70 years?

_____

How did I find Step 17? ☐ Easy ☐ OK ☐ Difficult

Step 18: Three- and four-digit × a multiple of 100 or 1000

Multiplying numbers by multiples of 100 or 1000 is similar to Step 17. Remember that when a number is multiplied by 100 the digits move two places to the left, and when multiplied by 1000 they move three places! So rather than one zero, use two or three!

What to do

$2814 \times 300 = ?$

1 If multiplying by a multiple of 100, first write a zero in the units and tens columns. If multiplying by a multiple of 1000, write a zero in the units, tens and hundreds columns.

HTh	TTh	Th	H	T	U
			2	8	1	4
×				3	0	0
					0	0

2 Then, as normal, multiply by the other digit (here multiply by 3), writing the numbers in the boxes to the left of the zeros.

			2	8	1	4
×				3	0	0
8	4	4	2	0	0
2		1			

Now you try

1

		1	7	9	5
×			3	0	0
			5	0	0
		1			

2

		1	3	9	7
×		5	0	0	0
		5	0	0	0

3

		6	4	1
×		4	0	0
			0	0

4

		1	2	4	2
×		7	0	0	0
			0	0	0

More practice   Each answer given below is wrong. Write what error has been made and then give the correct answer each time.

5

			2	5	9
×		7	0	0	0
1	8	1	3	0	0

Error: _____

Correct answer: _____

6

			9	4	2
×			8	0	0
7	5	3	6	0	0	0

Error: _____

Correct answer: _____

7

		4	8	7	4
×		2	0	0	0
8	7	4	8	0	0	0

Error: _____

_____

Correct answer: _____

8

		1	2	4	2
×		3	0	0
	7	2	6	0	0

Error: _____

_____

Correct answer: _____

Problem solving   Answer 'true' or 'false' to each question.

9 $4672 \times 100 = 467\,200$

_____

10 $1234 \times 2000 = 246\,800$

_____

11 $333 \times 3000 = 999\,000$

_____

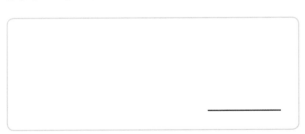

Final test Multiplying by one-digit numbers or by multiples of 10, 100 or 1000

Steps 15 to 18

1 $827 \times 20 = ?$

		8	2	7
×			2	0

2 $387 \times 30 = ?$

3 $374 \times 100 = ?$

		3	7	4
×		1	0	0

4 $2375 \times 800 = ?$

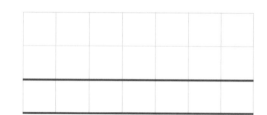

5 $5645 \times 3000 = ?$

			5	6	4	5
×			3	0	0	0

6 $34\,645 \times 900 = ?$

Steps 1 to 18 mixed

Use the grid below for working.

7 In Australia, a train travels at 124km per hour for five hours without stopping. How far does it travel in that time? _____

8 In her part-time job Julie earns £7563 each year. How much does she earn in three years? _____